# RIDDLE AROUND

Write the first letter of each object in the correct spaces.
Start reading at 1 to find the answer to this froggy funny.

## What is this frog's favorite holiday?

Illustrated by Jerry Zimmerman

# BOAT CODE

The names of some famous ships are flying in these flags. Use the code below to decipher the name of each. These flags show a real code that is used by boats and ships to send messages.

Illustrated by John Nez

# ROW, ROW, ROW

Each statue below has something in common with the two others in the same row. For example, in the top row across each statue features an animal. Look at the other rows across, down, and diagonally. Can you tell what each row of statues has in common?

Answer on page 47.

# DOT MAGIC

Connect the dots from 1 to 83 to find
someone who sticks her neck out.

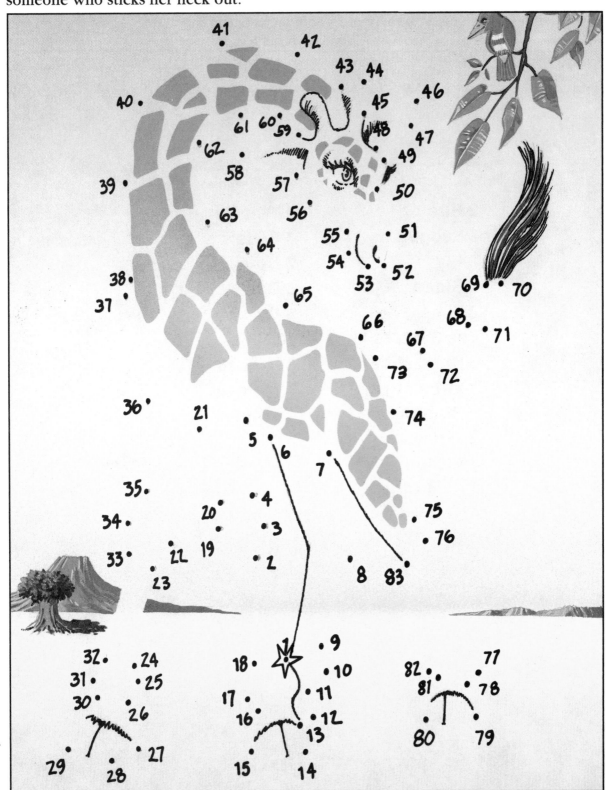

Illustrated by Tom Powers

# YOUR NUMBER'S UP

Your number's up, or down, backward, across, or diagonal. Look through the grid to find each of these numbered items. Numbers appear in the grid along with the words. Some letters and numbers will appear in more than one word. The uncircled letters spell out a word that tells what to do with numbers.

2 Bits

2 Legged

2 Ply

2 Sided

2 Timer

The 3 Bears

3 Blind Mice

3 Little Pigs

3 Ring Circus

3 Strikes

4 H Club

4 Leaf Clover

4 Square

4 Wheeler

7 Seas

7 Up

8 Ball

8 By 10

10 Pins

Sweet 16

40 Winks

50 States

Illustrated by Dominic Catalano

# BABY BLUNDERS

How many unusual things can you see in this picture?

Illustrated by R. Michael Palan

# FIREFIGHTER FRANK

Help Frank reach the truck to answer the alarm!

Answer on page 47.

# UP IN THE ATTIC

We were cleaning out the Puzzlemania attic and found a lot of different stuff. So we decided to use all of it in a puzzle. The items will fit into the grid in only one unique way. Use the size of each word as a clue to where it might fit. Words in parentheses are not included. We really appreciate your help straightening this up.

**4 Letters**
GIFT
HATS
LAMP
TOYS

**5 Letters**
BOOKS
CHAIR
CHEST
COINS
DOLLS
QUILT
SUITS
TOOLS

**6 Letters**
CRADLE
DISHES
HATBOX
MEDALS
PAPERS
STAMPS
TEAPOT

**7 Letters**
ANIMALS (stuffed)
BOTTLES
CLOTHES
JEWELRY
LETTERS
RECORDS

**8 Letters**
PICTURES
UNIFORMS

# A MUSICAL INTERLUDE

Number these pictures to show what happened first, second, and so on.

Answer on page 48.

# DESIGNER CLOTHES

Here's your chance to be a fashion plate. Design your own message on this brand-new T-shirt.

BOLLE
Special-
-TEE S

# HIDDEN PICTURES

There are at least 18 objects hidden in this picture. How many can you find?

# BUNNY HOP

Help the rabbit hop along the right path to reach his burrow. The symbols tell him which way to move.

move 1 space down

move 1 space up

move 1 space right

move 1 space left

Path 1  Path 2  Path 3  Path 4  Path 5  Path 6

Illustrated by Sherry Neidigh

Answer on page 48.

# STOP, LOOK, AND LIST

Under every category, list one thing that begins with each letter. For example, one thing that travels on water and begins with "R" is a Rowboat. Name another.

## THINGS THAT TRAVEL ON WATER

R _____

B _____

H _____

M _____

A _____

## THINGS THAT TRAVEL ON LAND

R _____

B _____

H _____

M _____

A _____

## THINGS THAT TRAVEL THROUGH AIR

R _____

B _____

H _____

M _____

A _____

Illustrated by Lisa Dayer

Answer on page 48.

# GLOBE PROBE

The renowned Gillner Museum has hired that world-famous adventurer, Dr. Cincinnati Holmes, to gather some exports from various countries. The museum gave Dr. Holmes a list of the products to look for, and now he must decide where to find them. It would be a big help if you could identify the country where each item will be found.

1. Ceramics

_____

2. Wool Sweaters

_____

3. Perfume

_____

4. Pottery

_____

5. Blankets

_____

6. Diamonds

_____

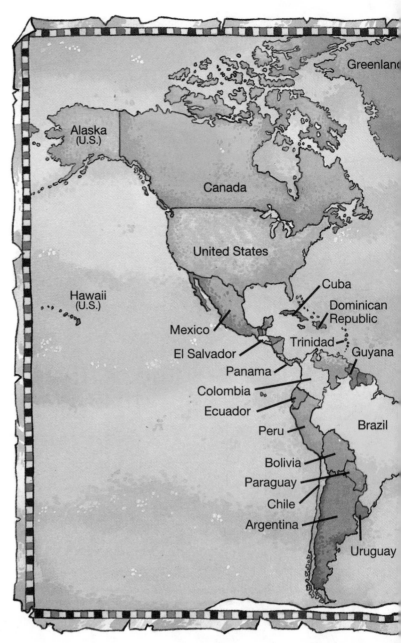

Answer on page 50.

7. Paper Fans

8. Boomerang

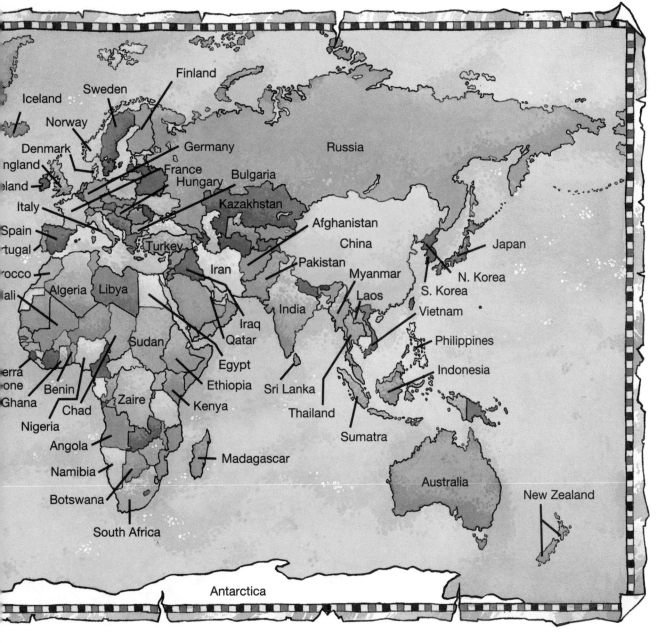

Iceland
Sweden
Norway
Finland
Denmark
Germany
ngland
France
Russia
eland
Hungary
Bulgaria
Italy
Kazakhstan
Spain
Turkey
Afghanistan
rtugal
China
Japan
rocco
Iran
Pakistan
N. Korea
ali
Algeria
Libya
Myanmar
S. Korea
India
Laos
Vietnam
Iraq
Sudan
Qatar
Philippines
erra
Egypt
Indonesia
one
Ethiopia
Benin
Sri Lanka
Ghana
Zaire
Kenya
Thailand
Chad
Nigeria
Sumatra
Angola
Namibia
Madagascar
Australia
Botswana
New Zealand
South Africa

Antarctica

# TIRED OUT

Can you tell who is inflating each object?

Answer on page 48.

Illustrated by Chuck Dillon

# WINNERS

You'll be a winner once you unscramble all these sports terms. After you've unscrambled them, see if you can name one sport or game associated with each term.

loga _____

rap _____

cores _____

nip _____

dontuchow _____

ehmo urn _____

lodg lamed _____

matchckee _____

strif capel _____

gink _____

Illustrated by Gregg Valley

Answer on page 48.

# WHOSE SIDE ARE THEY ON?

In this game of "Cops and Robbers," it's up to you to decide who's who. Put a good "G" next to those people who uphold the law. Put a big bad "B" next to those who are lawbreakers.

1. Sheriff _____

2. Police Officer _____

3. Bandit _____

4. Constable _____

5. Pirate _____

6. Marshal _____

7. Thug _____

8. Burglar _____

9. Detective _____

10. Outlaw _____

11. Thief _____

12. Inspector _____

13. Lawman _____

14. Highwayman _____

15. Deputy _____

16. Crook _____

Illustrated by Jerry Zimmerman

Answer on page 48.

# SKYDIVING MEMORIES

Take a long look at this picture. Try to remember everything you see in it. Then turn the page and answer some questions without looking back at the picture.

Illustrated by Kit Wray

DON'T READ THIS UNTIL YOU HAVE LOOKED AT "Skydiving Memories—Part 1" ON PAGE 25.

# SKYDIVING MEMORIES    Part 2

Can you answer these questions about the scene you saw? Don't peek!

1. How many planes were part of this jump?
2. Was the door on the lower plane open or closed?
3. Could anyone be seen in the planes?
4. Were there any animals in the scene?
5. How many parachutes were open?
6. What symbol was on the red jumpsuit?
7. What symbol was on the pink jumpsuit?
8. What was the serial number on the plane?

Answer on page 48.

# COMMON BONDS

What do these objects have in common?

Illustrated by Gregg Valley

Answer on page 48.

# SQUARE ROOTS

Place the numbers 1 through 9 in the boxes below, one number per box, so that the entire square follows these rules:

1. J, K, and L are three consecutive numbers in order, reading left to right.

2. J x L = Q.

3. P, Q, and R are three consecutive numbers in order, reading left to right.

4. O is the next number after N.

5. The two diagonal rows have the same sum when the numbers are added together.

Hint: Make a list of numbers from 1 through 9 and cross off each one as you place it in a square. The leftover number is M.

# PICTURE MIXER

Copy these mixed-up squares in the spaces on the next page to put this picture back together. The letters and numbers tell you where each square belongs. The first one, A-3, has been done for you.

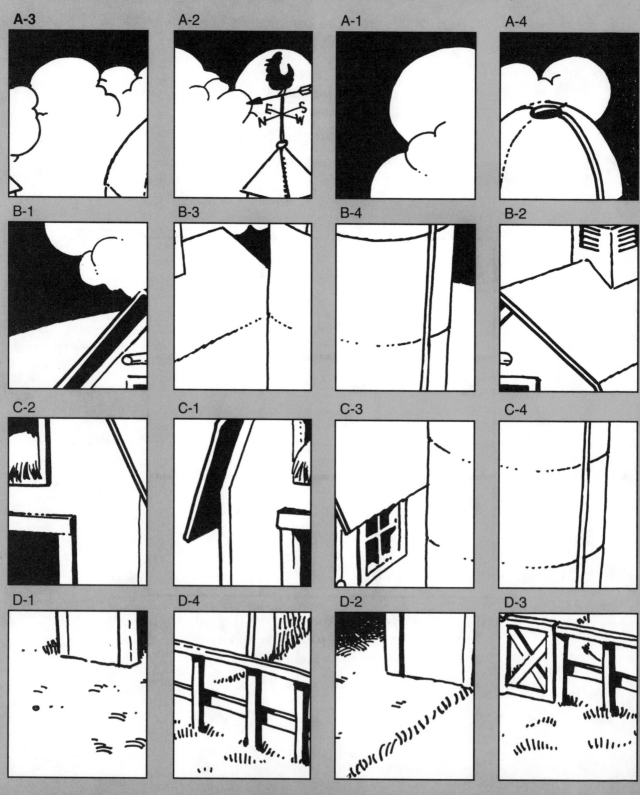

Illustrated by Tom Powers

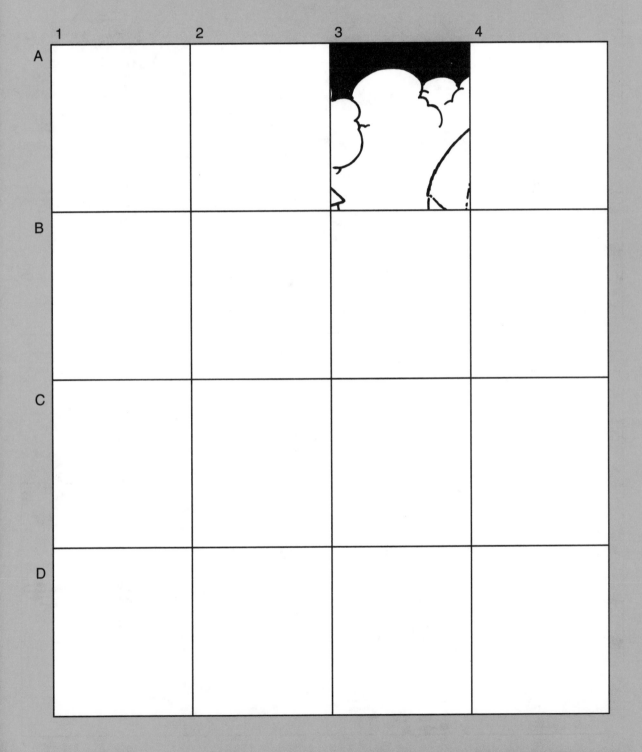

# ON YOUR MARK

How many differences can you see between these two pictures?

Illustrated by Mark Corcoran

# GO FOR IT!

Each word below contains the letters F-O-R.
See how many you can complete beFORe you FORget.

1. Dinner utensil:                             FOR __

2. 38th president of the United States:  FOR __

3. Sherwood or Black:                        FOR __ __ __

4. To be able to buy:                         __ __ FOR __

5. Amount of exertion put into something: __ __ FOR __

6. From a different country:                FOR __ __ __ __

7. Chinese cookie insert:                   FOR __ __ __ __

8. To soothe or pamper:                     __ __ __ FOR __

9. Baseball player's work clothes:         __ __ __ FOR __

10. Predict the weather:                     FOR __ __ __ __ __

11. The Golden State:                         __ __ __ __ FOR __ __ __

12. Researched facts:                         __ __ FOR __ __ __ __ __ __

Illustrated by Paul Richer

Answer on page 49.

# IT'S GOOD TO BE THE KING

Nobly step forward to answer the questions posed to thee.
Place thine answers in yon grid, and thou shalt be known
as a crossword peer.

## Across

1. The queen's husband
4. A nobleman found in *earlobe*
8. Before (in poems)
9. Edgar Allan _ _ _
10. East-southeast
11. The king's wife
13. Not cheerful or pleasant
15. Backbone
18. Otherwise
20. Noble title for Dracula
23. Northern Arizona University (abbreviation)
25. Noah's boat
26. To annoy
27. Device for winding fishing line
28. Short for Peter

## Down

1. Sharp
2. Internal Revenue Service (initials)
3. Requires
5. Large primate
6. Fish eggs
7. To loan
11. Bedcover
12. Large containers for coffee or flowers
14. Not closed
16. _ _ _ _ _, meenie, miney, mo
17. Mark where cut has healed
19. Nobleman ranked just below a prince
21. Rock which gives iron
22. Short for ukelele
24. Drawing and painting

Illustratéd by Charles Jordan

Answer on page 49.

# FOOD FIND

Something to eat is served up in each word on this menu. It's up to you to go along the buffet and pick out the food. No letters are scrambled or out of order. For example, in the word SKIPPERS, you will find kippers, which is a type of fish.

1. Appearance _____

2. Plump _____

3. Sliver _____

4. Coats _____

5. Exclamation _____

6. Pied _____

7. Salmonella _____

8. Scream _____

9. Breadth _____

10. Avarice _____

11. Beggar _____

12. Dappled _____

13. Aliment _____

14. Unicorn _____

15. Windjammer _____

16. Tease _____

17. Ashamed _____

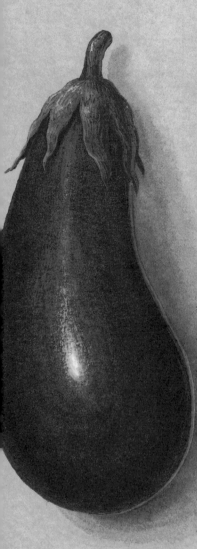

Illustrated by John Rice

Answer on page 49.

# INSTANT PICTURE

Fill in each section containing two dots to find the key to great harmony.

Answer on page 49.

# WHAT AILS YOU?

These people have come down with silly sicknesses related to their jobs. The doctor gave her nurse a list with a diagnosis for each patient. Unfortunately, she didn't write down who had what sickness. It's up to you to guess the profession of each person and then come up with the correct diagnosis for each. The nurse understands how to get started because yesterday the beekeeper had hives and the carpenter had a hangnail.

Flu
Charley horse
Wrenched arm
Broken limb
Salmonella
Calcium deposits
Shock
Slipped disc
Bone spurs
Ringworm

Answer on page 49.

# LETTER GETTER

All 26 letters of the alphabet are hidden somewhere in this picture.
How many can you find?

Illustrated by R. Michael Palan

# STUDY BUDDIES

Mrs. Olsen teamed four boys with four girls in her fifth grade class. Each team of one boy and one girl was assigned a different ancient civilization to study. From the clues below, can you determine which students worked together and what country each team was assigned?

Use the chart to keep track of your answers. Put "X" in each box that can't be true and "O" in the box where information matches. For example, clue 4 says Bob was not partnered with Nancy or Helen, so put Xs in the boxes where those names meet.

|        | Mary | Megan | Nancy | Helen | Bob | Mike | Rick | Henry |
|--------|------|-------|-------|-------|-----|------|------|-------|
| Egypt  |      |       |       |       |     |      |      |       |
| Rome   |      |       |       |       |     |      |      |       |
| Greece |      |       |       |       |     |      |      |       |
| China  |      |       |       |       |     |      |      |       |
| Bob    |      |       |       |       |     |      |      |       |
| Mike   |      |       |       |       |     |      |      |       |
| Rick   |      |       |       |       |     |      |      |       |
| Henry  |      |       |       |       |     |      |      |       |

*Illustrated by Anni Matsick*

1. Henry and his partner, who is not Nancy, studied ancient Egypt.

2. Mary, who is an Asian-American, was pleased to be able to study the homeland of her ancestors.

3. Helen and her partner, who is not Mike, studied the ancient Greeks.

4. Bob's partner was neither Nancy nor Helen.

Answer on page 49.

# DINING OUT

If you look around this diner, you'll find more than a good spot to eat. You'll find the answer to the riddle below. Follow the directions, and put the letters onto the numbered spaces to get your order filled.

---

**Where do smart frankfurters end up?**

___ ___　 ___ ___ ___　 ___ ___ ___ ___ ___　 ___ ___ ___ ___
1　 2　 　 3　 4　 5　 　 4　 1　 2　 1　 6　 　 6　 1　 7　 7

---

- Letter four is on top of the doughnuts.
- The coffeepot has letter two.
- A waitress has letter three in her hair.
- The horse at the counter is eating letter five.
- Letter seven is featured on the newspaper.
- Look for letter six with the Catch of the Day.
- Letter one is being flipped on the spatula.

Answer on page 49.

CATCH
of the
DAY

41

# HOLIDAY GRIDS

To find the names of some holidays, fill in the boxes
with the number of letters requested.

**1**

3/4 of half
1/2 of love
1/2 of well
2/5 of green

**2**

3/4 of that
3/5 of rinks
2/5 of magic
2/5 of vital
1/2 of sing

**3**

2/5 of china
1/3 of ribbon
1/2 of star
1/2 of masked

Illustrated by Joe Boddy

Answer on page 50.

# HOOK, LINES, AND THINKERS

You've got a license to fish the limit if you can find at least 40 words hiding in the letters of FISHERMAN. To be of the legal limit, each word will have only four letters.

# CHECK THE X

Xavier is very excited. All of his masterpieces are on display. He's also surrounded by many items that contain his favorite letter—"X." There are at least 24 objects here with an X in their names. How many can you see?

# THE END

All these words will fit in this grid in one unique way.
Use the size of each word as a clue to where it should end up.

ADIEU
BOTTOM
CABOOSE
COMPLETE
CONCLUSION
DONE
ENDING
EXPIRED

FINALE
FINE
FINISH
LAST
PERIOD
QUIT

Answer on page 50.

Illustrated by Jerry Zimmerman

# ANSWERS

## COVER

## RIDDLE AROUND (page 3)
What is this frog's favorite holiday?
Mudder's Day

## BOAT CODE (pages 4-5)
1. MAYFLOWER
2. CONSTITUTION
3. NIÑA
4. MAINE
5. PINTA
6. BOUNTY
7. MONITOR
8. TITANIC
9. HALF MOON
10. SANTA MARIA

## ROW, ROW, ROW (page 6)

Pieces missing    Instruments    Women    Circles

Animals

Name plates

Wings

Laurel crowns

## DOT MAGIC (page 7)

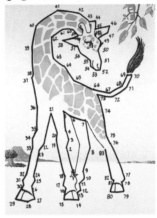

## YOUR NUMBER'S UP (pages 8-9)

Uncircled letters: COUNT

## FIREFIGHTER FRANK (page 11)

## UP IN THE ATTIC (pages 12-13)

```
        S           C           C       R   A
S U I T S       H A T B O X     E       A
        A       A           I   C       N
        M       I       U N I F O R M S  I
  C   P A P E R S       S       R    ■  A
  R   S   I               M E D A L S   S S
  A       C L O T H E S       S       S
  D       T       O           C       Q
J E W E L R Y   D O L L S   H A T S   U
        E       L E     T O Y S   L   I
  B O O K S   G     T         E   T E A P O T
        D I S H E S           M   M
        F           R         P
      B O T T L E S
```

## A MUSICAL INTERLUDE (page 14)

6  3
4  1
2  5

## BUNNY HOP (page 18)

## STOP, LOOK, AND LIST (page 19)

Here are our answers. You may have found others.

| THINGS THAT TRAVEL ON WATER | THINGS THAT TRAVEL ON LAND |
|---|---|
| Raft | Roller skate |
| Barge | Bicycle |
| Hydrofoil | Handcar |
| Motorboat | Motorcycle |
| Aircraft carrier | Automobile |

THINGS THAT TRAVEL THROUGH AIR
Rocket
Balloon
Helicopter
Missile
Airplane

## GLOBE PROBE (pages 20-21)

The answer appears on page 50.

## TIRED OUT (page 22)

1-C, 2-B, 3-D, 4-A

## WINNERS (page 23)

We listed only one sport for each answer. You may have found others.

| goal | (hockey) |
|---|---|
| par | (golf) |
| score | (soccer) |
| pin | (wrestling) |
| touchdown | (football) |
| home run | (baseball) |
| gold medal | (track and field) |
| checkmate | (chess) |
| first place | (racing) |
| king | (checkers) |

## WHOSE SIDE ARE THEY ON? (page 24)

| 1. G | 5. B | 9. G | 13. G |
|---|---|---|---|
| 2. G | 6. G | 10. B | 14. B |
| 3. B | 7. B | 11. B | 15. G |
| 4. G | 8. B | 12. G | 16. B |

## SKYDIVING MEMORIES (page 26)

| 1. Two | 5. Three |
|---|---|
| 2. Open | 6. Flag of U.S.A. |
| 3. Yes | 7. Heart |
| 4. No | 8. 398JM |

## COMMON BONDS (page 26)

None of these objects has moving parts.

## SQUARE ROOTS (page 27)

| J 2 | K 3 | L 4 |
|---|---|---|
| M 1 | N 5 | O 6 |
| P 7 | Q 8 | R 9 |

## PICTURE MIXER (pages 28-29)

## GO FOR IT! (page 31)

| | |
|---|---|
| 1. fork | 7. fortune |
| 2. Ford | 8. comfort |
| 3. forest | 9. uniform |
| 4. afford | 10. forecast |
| 5. effort | 11. California |
| 6. foreign | 12. information |

## IT'S GOOD TO BE THE KING (pages 32-33)

| | | | | | | |
|---|---|---|---|---|---|---|
| ¹K | ²I | ³N | G | ⁴E | ⁵A | ⁶R | ⁷L |

(crossword grid)

Row 1: K I N G ■ E A R L
Row 2: E R E ■ P O E
Row 3: E S E ■ Q U E E N ■ D
Row 4: N ■ D O U R ■ D
Row 5: ■ S P I N E ■
Row 6: S ■ E L S E ■ D
Row 7: C O U N T ■ N A U
Row 8: A R K ■ I R K
Row 9: R E E L ■ P E T E

## FOOD FIND (page 34)

| | |
|---|---|
| 1. pear | 10. rice |
| 2. plum | 11. egg |
| 3. liver | 12. apple |
| 4. oats | 13. lime |
| 5. clam | 14. corn |
| 6. pie | 15. jam |
| 7. salmon | 16. tea |
| 8. cream | 17. ham |
| 9. bread | |

## INSTANT PICTURE (page 35)

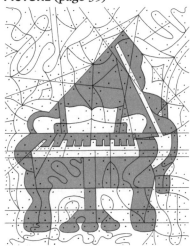

## WHAT AILS YOU? (pages 36-37)

1. Mechanic—Wrenched arm
2. Pilot—Flu
3. Electrician—Shock
4. Cowboy—Bone spurs
5. Tree surgeon—Broken limb
6. Milkman—Calcium deposits
7. Jockey—Charley horse
8. Fisherman—Salmonella
9. Jeweler—Ringworm
10. Computer programmer—Slipped disc

## STUDY BUDDIES (page 39)

Henry studied Egypt but NOT with Nancy (clue 1). Neither was his partner Mary (clue 2) nor Helen (clue 3); His partner was Megan.

Helen studied Greece (clue 3). Her partner was not Henry (see above), Mike (clue 3), nor Bob (clue 4). Helen's partner was Rick.

Mary studied China; this leaves Nancy, who studied ancient Rome. Bob was not Nancy's partner (clue 4), so he must have been teamed with Mary. That leaves Mike as Nancy's partner.

In summary:
Henry and Megan studied Egypt.
Rick and Helen studied Greece.
Bob and Mary studied China.
Nancy and Mike studied Rome.

## DINING OUT (pages 40-41)

Where do smart frankfurters end up?
ON THE HONOR ROLL

## HOLIDAY GRIDS (page 42)

1. Halloween
2. Thanksgiving
3. Christmas

## HOOK, LINES, AND THINKERS (page 43)

We found 42 words. You may have found others.
aims, amen, arms, ears, fair, fame, fans, fare,
farm, fear, fern, fine, fins, fire, firm, fish, hair,
hams, hare, harm, hire, main, mare, mash,
mesh, mine, mire, name, near, rain, rams, rash,
ream, rein, rise, same, sane, seam, sham, shim,
shin, sire

## THE END (page 46)

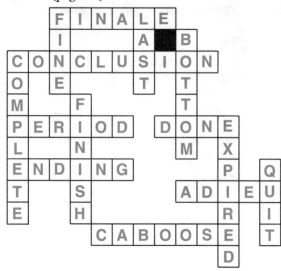

## GLOBE PROBE (pages 20-21)

1. Ceramics - China
2. Wool Sweaters - Ireland
3. Perfume - France
4. Pottery - Chile
5. Blankets - Colombia
6. Diamonds - South Africa
7. Paper Fans - Japan
8. Boomerang - Australia

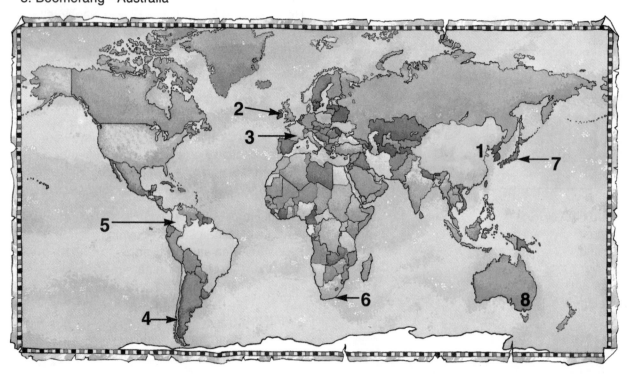